This book belongs to:

....

CONTENTS

STORIES BY IAN ROBINSON
(RUPERT AND THE GARDENS MYSTERY BY IAN ROBINSON AND JAMES HENDERSON)
ILLUSTRATED BY JOHN HARROLD
STORY COLOURING BY DORIS CAMPBELL

John Harrold.

RUPERT

THE DAILY EXPRESS ANNUAL

John Harrold.

Published by Annual Concepts Limited
One High Street, Princes Risborough, Buckinghamshire HP27 OAG

No 57

£4.75

RUPERT

*Rupert and Edward think they should
Find lots of conkers in the wood.*

It is a crisp autumn morning. Rupert and his friend, Edward Trunk, have decided to go out and look for conkers. The first trees they come to are already bare and all they can find are empty husks. "Never mind," says Rupert. "I know some more trees where we're bound to find some!" The pals have almost reached the second stand of trees when they see Willie Mouse running towards them. "Look!" he cries. "I've caught a leaf!"

and the Falling Leaf

*They start to search, but suddenly
They hear a voice cry, "Look at me!"*

*It's Willie Mouse, who tells them how
He caught a falling leaf just now.*

The two chums can't understand why Willie is so excited. "It looks so ordinary," shrugs Edward. "What's special about it, Willie?" "Nothing!" laughs the little mouse. "But I caught it before it touched the ground. If you catch a falling leaf you can make a wish, you know." "Can anyone wish?" asks Rupert. "Yes," says Willie. "But first they have to catch a falling leaf. Why don't you try? It's not as easy as it sounds . . ."

*"Try it," he tells the pals. "If you
Catch one, you'll each get a wish too."*

RUPERT CATCHES A LEAF

"I'll try my luck first," Edward calls
And jumps up as the first leaf falls.

He lunges forward with a cry –
Success! Now Rupert has a try . . .

"Bravo!" cries Willie eagerly.
"You've caught a leaf as well, I see!"

But Rupert's caught a note which pleads
For help. "H. E. L. P.!" he reads.

The pals agree to have a go and wait patiently for the next gust of wind. Before long a breeze starts to rustle the tops of the trees and soon there is a shower of golden leaves gliding gently down towards them. Edward tries to catch one straightaway, but the leaf he has chosen seems to swerve out of reach at the last moment! Lunging forward, he gives a cry of triumph and catches it with the tip of his trunk. "Well done!" laughs Rupert. "Now it's my turn to try . . ."

Rupert watches a leaf float slowly towards him. "Hooray!" he cries as he jumps up and catches it safely. He spins round to show the others but his smile fades and he gives a puzzled frown. "What's wrong?" asks Willie. "Look!" gasps Rupert. "It's not a leaf at all! It's a screwed up piece of paper with some writing on it. H . . E . . L . . P . . .Help!" The pals look worried. Someone's in trouble, but who can it be, and where can the mysterious note have come from?

RUPERT SPOTS A BALLOON

*"Who sent it?" Rupert asks. Then he
Looks up and points excitedly.*

*The air balloonist waves and then
Points down towards the ground again.*

*Then Rupert cries, "I understand!
The note says that he wants to land!"*

*The pals chase the balloon and see
A rope unfurling gradually.*

The pals peer up through the branches of the trees and are astonished to see an enormous balloon floating high above their heads. "It's a balloonist!" cries Rupert as a distant figure leans over the edge of the basket. He calls to the pals but is too far away to be heard above the noise of the wind in the trees. "Hello!" shouts Rupert and waves to him. The balloonist waves back to the pals, then seems to point downwards to the ground . . .

Puzzled by the balloonist's strange sign, Rupert looks at the note once more. "I wonder why he needs help?" he starts, then sees that there is a message written on the other side. "What does it say?" asks Willie. "He wants to land in Nutwood but can't come down because a valve has stuck!" reads Rupert. "He wants us to pull on a rope he's going to lower over the side . . ." "There it is!" cries Edward. "He's started to let it down from the basket."

RUPERT LENDS A HAND

"Let's pull together," Rupert cries
And runs to where the rope's end lies.

As soon as Rupert counts to three
The pals start pulling steadily . . .

The pilot starts to thank the friends
For all their help as he descends.

But then a rock makes Edward trip.
"Oh, no!" he cries. "I've lost my grip!"

Rupert, Willie and Edward run forward to catch the rope which the balloonist has lowered. Rupert reaches it first and tells the others to take a firm grip, as though they were getting ready for a tug of war. "We'll all pull together when I give the word," he explains. "Ready now? One . . two . . three, heave!" At first nothing seems to happen, then Edward turns and pulls on the rope with all his might. "That's it!" cries Rupert as the balloon starts to come down . . .

The three pals keep pulling on the rope until the basket is almost down. "I say, well done, you chaps!" calls the balloonist. "Frightfully decent of you to help me out like this . . ." Just at that moment Rupert feels the rope give a sudden lurch. He looks round and sees that Edward has tripped over a stone. "Oh, no!" he gasps as his friend topples forward, letting go of the rope. "I don't think Willie and I can hold the balloon steady all by ourselves!"

10

RUPERT AND WILLIE TAKE OFF

The chums hold tight, then realise
That the balloon's begun to rise!

Next moment they're both carried high
As up it shoots, into the sky.

Rupert explains their only hope
Is to climb up the trailing rope . . .

"Thank goodness!" the balloonist calls.
"Now quick, before your small friend falls!"

Try as they might, Rupert and Willie are far too light to stop the balloon from rising again. They tug on the rope as hard as they can, but are dragged forward and suddenly jerked off their feet! Before they realise what is happening, they have been lifted high into the air. "Come back!" calls Edward as he chases after them, but it is too late. The balloon has broken free and sails up into the sky with Rupert and Willie still clinging to the rope . . .

The pals have been carried so high they can't let go of the rope. All they can do now is try and clamber into the basket. "I c . . c . . can't!" wails Willie. "It's too far!" "Don't worry!" says Rupert. "Just hold on tight!" Shinning carefully up the rope, Rupert finally reaches the basket and is hauled aboard by the anxious balloonist. "What rotten luck!" he exclaims. "Thank goodness you're safe and sound!" "Yes," says Rupert. "But what about Willie?"

11

RUPERT'S JOURNEY BEGINS

He hauls the rope with all his might
As Rupert calls out, "Hold on tight!"

"Well done!" cries the balloonist when
At last, poor Willie's safe again.

He sighs and tells the pals why they
Can't land in Nutwood straightaway.

"I've had a piece of rotten luck:
The valve that works the gas tank's stuck!"

Willie is too frightened to move. "Don't look down!" calls Rupert. "Just close your eyes and hang on!" "That's the ticket!" says the balloonist and begins to pull on the rope. "W . . what's happening?" asks Willie. "I don't think I can last out much longer!" "There's no need!" laughs Rupert as he grabs hold of the trembling mouse and starts to haul him over the side of the basket. " You're safe now, old chap!" says the balloonist. "Sorry you had such a fright!"

Now that the pals are safely aboard, the pilot tells them why he's come to Nutwood. "This is a brand new balloon which runs on gas from the cylinder here by the basket. I was on my way to show it to my friend, the Old Professor, when the cylinder valve jammed open! Now, I'm afraid, the balloon won't come down until it runs out of gas . . ." "How long will that take?" asks Rupert. "Hard to say really," shrugs the balloonist. "This is her first proper flight . . ."

12

RUPERT FLIES ABOVE THE CLOUDS

"Look!" Rupert cries as up they go.
"There's Nutwood, spread out down below . . ."

A wind starts and the two pals find
They've soon left Nutwood far behind.

They soar up through the clouds and see
The sun is shining brilliantly.

"It seems we're heading South, although
Exactly where, I just don't know!"

The balloon climbs higher and higher, until Rupert and Willie can see the whole of Nutwood spread out below them, like a giant map. "Look!" cries Rupert. "There's the church tower . . . and that's my house!" A strong wind carries the chums away from the village and over the nearby fields. Soon they have lost sight of Nutwood altogether and fly on, past unknown woods and hills. The balloon keeps rising higher and higher, until it starts to disappear up into the clouds.

As the basket of the balloon rises up through the clouds, the pals find themselves enveloped in a damp, cold mist. "It's j . . just like fog!" shivers Willie. The next moment they break through the clouds and emerge into dazzling golden sunshine. "That's better!" cries the balloonist. He takes out a compass and studies it carefully. "We seem to be heading South," he declares. "Can't say any more than that for the moment. Bit of a mystery tour, I'm afraid . . ."

RUPERT FALLS TOWARDS THE SEA

"I hope you chaps will both agree
To join me in a cup of tea!"

But as the pals begin to drink
They feel the basket start to sink . . .

"I really must apologise,
We're out of gas!" the pilot cries.

Next moment they plunge rapidly
Down through the clouds, towards the sea!

As there is nothing more to be done, Rupert and Willie decide to make the most of their unexpected flight. "Splendid sight, isn't it!" enthuses the balloonist as they gaze down at the fleecy white clouds. "I say," he adds, producing a large thermos flask from a wicker hamper, "anyone for a cup of tea?" Just as he's finished pouring out the tea, the basket gives a sudden lurch and starts to drop rapidly. "Oh, no!" gasps Rupert. "What's happening?"

"The gas cylinder must have run out!" cries the balloonist. "I had hoped we'd get a bit more warning. Never mind, at least we'll soon be able to see where we are!" As the balloon sinks below the clouds once more, Rupert and Willie give a gasp of surprise. Instead of more trees and hills, there is a vast expanse of water glinting below them. "It's the sea!" cries Willie. "Hold on tight!" orders the balloonist. "We're about to land in the drink!"

RUPERT LANDS WITH A SPLASH

The basket lands, then starts to float
Upon the waves, just like a boat!

"Quick lads!" the pilot calls. "Undo
The ropes and all the sandbags too."

"I'll just look through my telescope.
We can't be far from land, I hope!"

There's nothing there, then Rupert spies
A dot. "Perhaps that's where land lies?"

The next moment the basket hits the water with a tremendous splash. "Quick!" calls the balloonist, "Untie all the ropes! We have to get clear of the deflated balloon before it starts to sink . . ." The pals do as they are told and are soon helping the balloonist untie the last sandbag. "Well done!" he declares. "We're quite safe now. The basket is designed to float, just like a small boat." "Good!" says Rupert. "But what are we going to do now?"

"The first thing we have to do is sight land!" the balloonist declares. Rupert and Willie peer hopefully into the distance, but all they can see is water on every side. "If only we had a telescope," sighs Willie. "But we have!" cries the balloonist and starts to rummage in the depths of the basket. Putting the telescope to his eye, he begins to scan the horizon slowly. "Nothing at all!" he shrugs at last. "Wait!" calls Rupert. "Try looking over here . . ."

RUPERT REACHES AN ISLAND

*"Yes!" cries the pilot. "I can see
An island there, quite definitely!"*

*"Aha! My trusty cricket bat!
I'll paddle us ashore with that!"*

*The pilot rows with all his might
And soon the island comes in sight.*

*"I've never seen such trees before!"
Says Rupert as he steps ashore.*

The balloonist turns to where Rupert is pointing. He peers intently through his telescope at the tiny black speck on the horizon. "It's an island!" he cries. "That's splendid! All we have to do now is find a way of rowing ashore!" As the basket bobs about on the waves, the balloonist thinks hard; then, to the pals' astonishment, he produces a cricket bat from the bottom of the basket. "Almost forgot I had it on board!" he tells the chums. "Just the thing for a makeshift paddle . . ."

Crouching down low in the basket, the balloonist begins to paddle with the bat as fast as he can. "It's working!" cries Rupert as they draw steadily nearer to the tiny island. Sure enough, the basket soon runs aground with a loud scrunch. Rupert clambers ashore. "How odd," he gasps. "The whole island seems to be covered in these strange trees . . ." "You're right!" agrees the balloonist as he helps Willie from the basket. "We must have drifted further south than I'd thought!"

RUPERT IS WOKEN BY A MONKEY

"We'll build a shelter for the night.
Let's gather palm leaves while it's light . . ."

As soon as they complete the task
It's time for more tea from the flask.

Next morning Rupert's woken by
A monkey's shrill, excited cry.

It grabs his scarf and runs away.
"Come back!" cries Rupert in dismay.

The tropical island where the pals have landed seems to be completely deserted. "There isn't time to explore much today," says the balloonist. "We have to build some sort of shelter before it gets dark . . ." Gathering a pile of driftwood from the beach, he tells Rupert and Willie to collect as many palm leaves as they can. Little by little the shelter takes shape until, at last, the pals add the final leaf to its roof. "Well done!" cries the balloonist. "Now for a spot of supper!"

Next morning, Rupert is suddenly woken by somebody tugging his scarf. "W . .what's the matter?" he murmurs. To his astonishment, he sees that the shelter is surrounded by chattering monkeys, one of which is pulling as hard as it can at the end of his scarf. "Stop that!" cries Rupert, but the next moment the monkey has seized the scarf and scampered away with it to the top of a tall palm tree. "Come back!" calls Rupert and begins to climb after him . . .

RUPERT SPOTS A SHIP

Then, climbing up a tall palm tree,
He spots a ship, far out to sea . . .

He tells the pilot, who says they
Must build a bonfire straightaway.

"That's it!" he cries. "The smoke will show
Them someone's here, before they go . . ."

It seems that they're in time, and yet
Each match the pilot strikes is wet!

Rupert climbs up the tree after the monkey who has taken his scarf, but the little creature is too quick for him and soon gets away. As he looks around, Rupert catches a glimpse of the sea and gives a sudden cry of surprise. "There's a ship on the horizon!" he calls and slides back down to join the others. "No time to lose!" cries the balloonist. "We must build a big fire straightaway. If we're lucky, the smoke will attract the crew's attention and they'll come to see who's here . . ."

Rupert and Willie run back to the shelter to gather armfuls of leaves, while the balloonist collects as much driftwood as he can find. Before long they are ready to light the bonfire they have built by the water's edge . . . The balloonist feels in his jacket pockets and produces a box of matches. He takes one out and strikes it. Nothing happens! He tries again, but still the matches won't light. "That's torn it!" he exclaims. "They must have got wet when we came ashore!"

RUPERT AND WILLIE GO EXPLORING

There's nothing that the chums can do
But watch the ship sail out of view . . .

To pass the time they all agree
To search the island thoroughly.

The two pals gather fruit but then
Spot Rupert's stolen scarf again!

As Rupert chases through the trees
He gasps aloud at what he sees . . .

Unable to light the fire they've built, the pals watch forlornly as the ship steams past the little island. "Come back!" calls Willie, but the ship just sails on out of sight. "Never mind, old chap!" says the balloonist. "There's bound to be another one soon. Let's go and explore the rest of the island while we're waiting . . . I'll go this way," he declares. "While you two can go off in the other direction. That way we can meet up later and tell each other what we've found . . ."

Rupert and Willie set off round the island, only to find that it is even more overgrown than they had thought. They have just begun to gather some fruit to eat later when Rupert spots two monkeys squabbling over something. "It's my scarf!" he cries and hurries forward to try to get it back. As soon as Rupert draws near, one of the monkeys snatches the scarf and scampers off into the jungle. Rupert runs after him through the trees, then gasps aloud at what he sees . . .

RUPERT DISCOVERS A RUINED TEMPLE

"A ruined temple!" Willie cries,
Unable to believe his eyes.

"Look!" Rupert calls to Willie. "There's
The monkey, climbing up those stairs!"

He's gone, but Willie starts to laugh
For left behind is Rupert's scarf . . .

A secret door swings open wide
Revealing a bright light inside.

"W . . what is it?" asks Willie as he follows Rupert into the jungle. "I don't know," says Rupert, gazing at the strange building before them. "It looks a bit like some sort of ancient temple, but it must have been hidden away like this for years and years . . ." At that moment, the pals catch sight of the monkey, who is climbing the steps of the temple, still clutching Rupert's scarf. "Come on, Willie!" calls Rupert. "Let's see if we can catch him!"

Rupert and Willie run to the top of the stairs but the monkey has vanished. "I wonder where he went?" asks Rupert. "Look!" cries Willie, "It's your scarf! There must be a secret entrance which the monkey used to escape but dropped your scarf as he went." Rupert looks carefully at the walls of the temple. "Perhaps if I push this stone . . ." he suggests. All at once there is the rumbling sound of a heavy door swinging open and the pals are dazzled by a brilliant light.

RUPERT FINDS A MIRROR

Inside the temple the pals find
A shining mirror of some kind . . .

"No," Rupert smiles. "I think we're wrong,
It's not a mirror, but a gong!"

They carry back the gong to where
The pilot said he'd meet the pair.

Rupert explains that they could try
To signal ships as they sail by . . .

At first the pals are too startled to move, but when they shield their eyes they can see that the dazzling light is coming from a giant mirror. "Why is it shining in the dark?" asks Willie. Rupert peers all round. "Look!" he cries. "the sunlight is shining down through a hole in the roof!" He lifts up the mirror and a strange ringing sound echoes round the temple. "It's not a mirror, it's a gong!" he gasps. "Let's carry it back with us. I think it might be just what we need!"

Although the gong is quite heavy, the pals manage to carry it back between them and arrive just in time to meet the balloonist, who is astonished to see what they have found. He is fascinated to learn of the ruined temple, but looks puzzled when Rupert explains that he wants to use the gong to signal to ships. "They'll be too far away to hear," he shrugs. "I don't want to *strike* it!" says Rupert. "I thought we could use it as a mirror to signal with the sun . . ."

RUPERT SENDS AN SOS

"I say!" the pilot cries. "Of course!
We'll send an SOS in Morse!"

Then Willie gives a cry of joy.
"On the horizon – ship ahoy!"

Tilting the gong to catch the light
Rupert hopes that their signal's right . . .

"Oh dear," sighs Rupert. "No reply!
Perhaps there's time for one more try?"

"I say," cries the balloonist. "What a good idea! I only hope I can remember enough Morse code to send the proper message. I'm a bit out of practice, I'm afraid." "It's S.O.S. isn't it?" asks Rupert. "That's right," declares the balloonist. "And to send that we need three short flashes, followed by three long ones, then three short flashes again . . . or is it the other way round?" "Look!" cries Willie suddenly. "There's another ship on the horizon. Let's see if Rupert's idea will work . . ."

There is not a moment to lose. Rupert and the balloonist lift up the gong and hurry down to the water's edge. Standing it upright, the balloonist starts to tilt it backwards and forwards so that it sends flashes of light out across the sea. "Three short," he counts. "Now three long . . . and three short flashes to finish!" "I wonder if they've seen us?" asks Willie. "There's no way of telling!" shrugs the balloonist. "Come on, Rupert. Let's try again!"

RUPERT AND WILLIE ARE RESCUED

This time a clear response appears
"They've spotted us!" the pilot cheers.

He peers towards the ship. "Hurray!
A rescue boat is on the way . . ."

The chums all hurry down to reach
The boat as it draws near the beach.

The pilot tells his story to
The rescue boat's astonished crew.

Has anyone on board the ship seen the balloonist's signal? At first nothing happens, but then a bright light flashes across the water, "Message received – Stand by." "Hurray!" cries Rupert. "It worked!" "Well done, chaps!" laughs the balloonist and starts to dance for joy. Leaving the pals to wait on the shore, he hurries back to the basket and returns clutching his telescope. "What's happening?" asks Rupert. "They're sending out a rescue boat!" the balloonist replies.

"Ahoy there!" cries the balloonist as the little boat draws near. Running to the water's edge, he introduces Rupert and Willie to the astonished sailors and explains how they came to be stranded on the tiny island. "We came as soon as we saw your signal!" an officer declares. "It was clever of you to think of using a mirror to send a message." "Oh, that was Rupert's idea!" smiles the balloonist. "He and Willie found the mirror, all I had to do was to try and remember my Morse code!"

RUPERT CLIMBS ABOARD

Then back towards the ship they row
With the balloon basket in tow.

A ladder's lowered down so they
Can climb aboard without delay.

The wireless operator sends
A call to Nutwood for the friends.

The captain says, "I'd like you three
To come and have a meal with me!"

The pals clamber aboard the rescue boat and are soon being rowed out towards the waiting ship. "Jolly kind of you to bring my basket back too!" says the balloonist. "It would have been a pity to just leave it there for the monkeys to play with!" As soon as the rowing boat reaches the ship there is a shrill whistle and a rope ladder is lowered over the side. "Prepare to receive visitors!" calls one of the sailors and steadies the ladder for the friends to climb.

The moment the pals are safely aboard, the balloonist asks if he can send a message to the Old Professor to let everyone in Nutwood know that Rupert and Willie are safe. "Of course!" says the officer and leads the way to the wireless room. As soon as the message has been sent, he takes the friends to meet the Captain. "So, you're the island castaways," he chuckles. "Sit down and join me for dinner. I want to hear all about your adventures . . ."

RUPERT AND WILLIE NEAR LAND

Next day the captain says he'll show
The two pals where the ship will go.

"Look!" Rupert cries excitedly.
"I think that may be land I see!"

"Your telescope," asks Rupert. "May
We take it on deck straightaway?"

Then, peering to the shore, the pair
See someone they know waiting there . . .

Next morning, Rupert and Willie are woken by bright sunlight streaming in through the porthole of their cabin. They hurry up on to the bridge, where the balloonist and the Captain are studying a large map. "We should catch sight of the coast soon," says the Captain. "Why don't you two go and keep a look out?" The pals run to the front of the ship and peer excitedly into the distance. For a long time they can see nothing but sea. Then Rupert gives a sudden cry, "Land ahoy!"

"You're right!" cries Willie. "I see it too! Let's go and borrow the balloonist's telescope!" Taking it in turns to look through the lens, the pals see the ship is approaching a distant harbour. "There are lots of people waiting down by the quayside!" calls Rupert. "Look, Willie. I can see a car there that's just like the Old Professor's . . ." "It *is* his car!" cries Willie. "There he is now . . . and Edward too! They must have come all the way from Nutwood to meet us . . ."

RUPERT BRINGS BACK A PRESENT

"Professor!" Rupert starts to yell,
Then sees that Edward's there as well . . .

The Old Professor says that they should
All come with him, back to Nutwood.

The Bears are both delighted when
They see that Rupert's safe again.

He's brought his parents back a treat –
A souvenir that they can eat!

"Professor! Edward!" calls Rupert and waves his scarf for them to see. "Thank goodness you're safe!" cries his old friend as the pals run down the gangway. "When Edward told me what had happened, I wondered how we'd ever manage to find you . . ." "Hello, Professor," says the balloonist. "I'm afraid there isn't much of the new balloon I wanted you to see . . ." "Never mind," smiles the old man. "Come back to Nutwood and we'll soon get you airborne again!"

The pals climb into the Professor's car and are soon speeding back to Nutwood. Mr. and Mrs. Bear are overjoyed to see that Rupert and Willie are safe and sound. "We landed on a tropical island!" Rupert tells them. "Some monkeys stole my scarf, then we found a ruined temple . . . and a huge gong. And look what else I found!" "Well I never!" chuckles Mr. Bear. "Fancy going out to look for conkers and finding . . . a pineapple!" The End.

Here are two different pictures of Rupert for you to colour in . . .

RUPERT and

*Rupert and Bill decide that they
Will go out picnicking one day.*

It is a lovely summer's day and Rupert and Bill have taken a picnic lunch and gone for a long walk. As they make their way through the fields which surround Nutwood, they come across a large flock of sheep. "They must be jolly hot under all that wool!" says Bill as he looks at a group huddled together in the shade of a big tree. "Not like the others over there," replies Rupert. "They've already been shorn for the summer . . ."

28

the Wool Gatherers

Crossing a field of sheep, they see
An unshorn group beneath a tree.

Then, suddenly, the two pals hear
An angry shout from somewhere near.

The pals continue towards a gate at the far end of the field, but are stopped in their tracks by a sudden angry shout. "I've got you now!" someone bellows gruffly, and a high, thin voice starts to wail, "Oh, no, please, you don't understand!" "What's going on?" cries Bill. "I don't know!" says Rupert. "It seems to be coming from the next field."Creeping forward, the pals peer through a gap in the hedge and gasp at what they see . . .

"Look through the hedge, Bill!" Rupert cries,
Unable to believe his eyes . . .

RUPERT SEES AN ARGUMENT

There stands the farmer, arguing
With one of Nutwood's Imps of Spring.

"You stole my wool!" the farmer cries
And points to where a small sack lies.

And, sure enough, the sack is full
Of newly-gathered wisps of wool.

"It's mine!" the Imp starts to protest
But Farmer Brown is not impressed.

On the far side of the hedge stands the farmer, who has seized hold of a little man. Rupert recognises him as one of Nutwood's Imps of Spring. "What's the matter?" he asks. "Someone has been stealing the wool from my sheep!" declares the farmer. "I was going to shear them next week, but it seems this Imp has beaten me to it and carried off all the wool." "It wasn't me!" cries the Imp. "Then how do you explain this?" says the farmer and points to a small sack.

The farmer tells the pals to take a look in the sack while he keeps hold of the struggling Imp. Sure enough, it is completely full of newly-gathered wool. "This *proves* you're the one who stole my wool!" the farmer cries. "I've caught you red-handed!" "It's not what you think!" the Imp protests, but the farmer silences him with an angry snort. "We'll let Constable Growler decide about that!" he snaps and marches the Imp off towards Nutwood without another word.

RUPERT SPOTS A CLUE

*"How strange!" says Rupert. "There's much more
To this than meets the eye, I'm sure!"*

*Then, by the gate, the two pals see
Some tracks have been made recently . . .*

*While searching for clues, Rupert hears
His name called as an Imp appears!*

*"We need your help," he tells the pair.
"My friend's not guilty, I declare!"*

"I don't believe it!" cries Rupert. "I know the Imps of Spring get up to all kinds of mischief, but I'm sure they would never steal from anyone." "But what was the Imp doing with that sack?" asks Bill. "And if he didn't take the rest of the farmer's wool, then who did?" "I don't know . . ." replies Rupert and looks thoughtfully at the soft ground near the gate. "Look at this!" he cries. "I'm sure these tracks were made by something heavy turning into the field . . ."

The two pals are still examining the strange tracks when, all of a sudden, somebody calls Rupert's name. He looks up and sees a second Imp of Spring, who has come to look for his missing partner. The Imp is appalled when he hears what has happened and says the farmer has made a big mistake. "The sack of wool might look as if it was stolen," he says, "but I promise it wasn't. Follow me. I have something to show you that will explain everything!"

RUPERT AND BILL GO UNDERGROUND

*"Please follow me," he says. "We're bound
For Imp Headquarters, underground."*

*The Imp stops by a little door
Marked, "Please knock". "It's our woollens store!"*

*Small sacks of wool fill half the room
While Imps sit spinning by a loom . . .*

*"We gather wisps throughout the year
To make our winter clothing here."*

Leading Rupert and Bill to an old oak tree, the Imp pulls open a little door and takes them down some steep steps to a tunnel, which Rupert soon recognises as part of the Imps' underground Kingdom. "Our work is nearly over for another year," the Imp explains. "But before we hand over to the Autumn Elves, we have to prepare for our long winter sleep. That's why we were out gathering wool in the farmer's fields . . ." he adds, as they come to a door marked, "Woollens – please knock".

Behind the door is a crowded workshop full of Imps, all busy spinning and weaving. There are lots of small sacks piled up in one corner, and each of them is full to the top with wool. "So the farmer was right!" gasps Bill. "No!" shouts the Imp above the clatter of the loom. "All this wool has been gathered from wisps caught on hedges and fences. We Imps have always taken it to make into blankets and night-shirts to keep us nice and warm through the long winter months . . ."

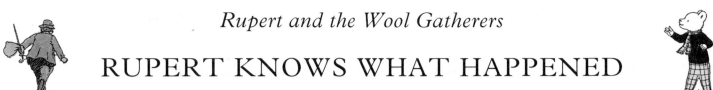

"The wool thieves struck last night, but then
We thought they were the farmer's men . . ."

"Gosh!" Rupert cries. "Those tracks we saw
Were left there by their van, I'm sure!"

"The farmer's wrong, but even so,
I doubt he'll let the first Imp go . . ."

Bill says he thinks the real crooks might
Come back to shear more sheep tonight!

"So that explains your friend's sack!" says Rupert as the Imp leads the way out of the workshop. "But who stole the wool from the farmer's flock?" "I don't know," the Imp replies. "Last night I saw some men carrying lanterns and thought it was the farmer and his men, checking on the sheep. Now I'm sure it was a gang of thieves! They must have waited until it was dark . . ." "And taken the wool away in a lorry!" breaks in Rupert, remembering the strange tracks he found near the gate.

"I was sure you couldn't have stolen the farmer's wool!" says Rupert as they walk back along the corridor. "But what about P.C. Growler?" asks the Imp. "It will take more than a few tyre tracks to convince him that the farmer has made a mistake!" The pals think hard, then Bill has a sudden idea. "Only *half* the flock has been shorn so far," he declares. "Perhaps the crooks will come back tonight to finish off the rest. Why don't we try to catch them in the act . . .?"

RUPERT HAS A PLAN

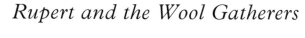

"Keep watching from the hollow tree!
We'll come and join you, after tea."

The pals run quickly as they can
While Rupert tells Bill of his plan . . .

Then later he shows Mrs. Bear
A sight that makes her gasp and stare.

"A wooden sheep!" she laughs. "Bless me!
It looks as lifelike as can be . . ."

The Imp thinks that Bill's idea is a good one. "We Imps can keep watch from the hollow tree," he volunteers. "Good!" says Rupert. "Bill and I will come and meet you here after tea."

"No one will see the Imps," says Bill as the pals hurry home, "but where are we going to hide? The crooks are bound to notice anything suspicious." "I've already thought of that," replies Rupert. "I think I know how we can avoid being spotted. Come on! I'll show you what I've got in mind . . ."

As soon as the pals reach Rupert's house they hurry away to Mr. Bear's garden shed. After a lot of sawing and hammering, Rupert calls for his mother to come and see what they've been up to. She hurries out into the garden and gives a cry of surprise. "I don't believe it. There's a sheep on the lawn!" "It worked!" laughs Rupert and explains how he and Bill set about making the wooden sheep. "All we have to do now," he adds, "is to try it out in a field!"

RUPERT AND BILL KEEP WATCH

The Imp's surprised by the sheep too
And asks what Rupert plans to do . . .

The two pals crouch down, side by side,
And show him how they mean to hide.

Then, after what seems a long wait
A lorry drives up to the gate . . .

"The crooks!" gasps Bill. "So I was right,
They've come to steal more wool tonight!"

The pals wheel the wooden sheep across the field towards the hollow tree where they agreed to meet the Imp of Spring. As they approach, a small door swings open and the Imp hurries out to meet them. Rupert explains that he and Bill plan to hide behind the sheep until the crooks arrive. "As soon as they do, we'll go and fetch Growler," he says. "This time he'll be able to catch the *real* thieves!" "Good luck!" calls the Imp as the pals crouch down out of sight . . .

After waiting for what seems like ages, the pals begin to think the crooks might not come back after all. It has started to grow dark when they suddenly hear the sound of an engine. "It's a lorry!" hisses Bill. "They've turned off the headlights to avoid being seen!" The lorry turns into the field and stops at the far end. As the pals peer towards it they can see some shadowy figures carrying lamps. "It's just as the Imp said!" gasps Rupert.

35

"*I'm going closer, Bill, to see*
What they do next. Wait here for me!"

Then Rupert slowly starts to creep
Towards the van, wheeling his sheep . . .

As Rupert looks, he sees a man
Herd unshorn sheep into the van.

But then he sees, without a doubt,
It's new-shorn sheep that scamper out!

The pals can see men with lanterns moving about at the far end of the field, but it's far too dark for them to see what the thieves are up to. "Stay here," Rupert tells Bill. "I'm going to try to get a closer look. As soon as I know how many men there are, we'll go and tell Growler what's happening." Bill agrees, but warns Rupert to keep well hidden behind the wooden sheep. "Don't worry!" whispers Rupert, and starts to creep slowly towards the lorry . . .

Rupert's plan works perfectly. In the darkness the wooden sheep looks so convincing that nobody notices him moving closer and closer to the lorry. As he gets nearer, he sees that the tailgate has been lowered and a heavy curtain drawn across the open gap. One of the men herds the sheep towards the ramp and into the lorry. A few moments later, the same sheep skip out again, completely shorn of all their wool! "They're shearing the sheep inside the lorry!" gasps Rupert.

RUPERT IS CAPTURED

*"I must tell Bill!" he thinks, but then
He's spotted by one of the men!*

*"There's only one thing we can do,
That's put him in the lorry too . . ."*

*Inside the van sit two men who
Shear each sheep as it passes through.*

*The third man ties up Rupert so
He can't escape before they go.*

"I must tell Bill what's happening!" thinks Rupert. As he moves he trips, knocks over the wooden sheep, and is immediately spotted by another member of the gang. "Not so fast!" shouts the man and seizes hold of Rupert. "You've been snooping around here, haven't you!" he growls. "Well, we can't risk having you go and tell the farmer everything you've seen!" With that he pulls across the curtain and bundles Rupert into the back of the lorry.

To Rupert's surprise, the inside of the van is like a small workshop, lit with two oil lamps which hang from the roof. Two men are busily shearing sheep and the floor is piled high with freshly-shorn wool. The third man pushes Rupert past the shearing benches to the back of the lorry and produces a length of rope from behind a pile of old sacks. "This will make sure you don't run off before we've finished!" he mutters and ties Rupert up securely.

RUPERT IS SET FREE

Then, finally, the men decide
To leave, with Rupert still inside!

Before they set off, Rupert hears
His name whispered, then Bill appears . . .

"I knew there must be something wrong
Because you had been gone so long!"

Then, suddenly, the pals find they
Can feel the lorry pitch and sway!

Rupert looks on helplessly while the men finish shearing the rest of Farmer Brown's sheep. As they load the wool into sacks they discuss what to do with him. "Plenty of time to sort that out later!" their leader declares. "We've finished here for tonight, so let's be under way." The men leave Rupert and go round to the front of the lorry. Almost at once Rupert hears somebody whisper his name. The canvas flap is pulled aside and a familiar face appears above the tailgate . . .

Bill scrambles up into the van and wastes no time in setting Rupert free. "I guessed that something had gone wrong when you took so long to come back, " he whispers. "I've already been to tell Growler what's happening and he's on his way, with some extra men from Nutchester." "Thank goodness!" breathes Rupert. "All we need to do now is . . ." As he speaks the engine roars into life and the van lurches forward. "Oh, no!" gasps Bill. "They're driving away!"

RUPERT AND BILL JOIN THE CHASE

The men drive off, but luckily,
The chums just manage to jump free.

Before the van's gone very far,
The two pals spot a speeding car . . .

"Come on!" calls Growler, with a grin,
"We'll catch the thieves! You two hop in . . ."

"Look!" Growler tells the chums. "You see,
We're gaining on them rapidly!"

Luckily, the field is too bumpy for the lorry to go very fast and the pals manage to jump clear before it begins to gather speed. They pick themselves up and chase after the crooks as they turn out of the gate at the top of the field. "They're going to get away before Growler arrives!" groans Bill as he watches the lorry speed off. "Look!" cries Rupert. "Someone else is coming this way. I can see their headlights getting nearer. They must be driving very fast!"

The car pulls up with a screech of brakes. Inside are P.C. Growler and a police driver. A second car follows close behind. "Hop in," calls Growler. "We're going to catch these wool thieves of yours!" The pals clamber into the car and are soon speeding along a narrow country lane in hot pursuit of the crooks' van. "There they are!" cries Growler and points to the lorry's tail-lights glowing in the distance. "We're gaining on them fast . . ."

RUPERT FINDS THE THIEVES

"Stop by this farm!" says Growler. "For
The crooks' van turned in here, I'm sure."

As Growler's men search all around,
Rupert finds wool wisps on the ground!

"I think we've caught those thieves of yours!"
Says Growler. "Open the barn doors!"

The doors swing open with a bang
And there, red-handed, stand the gang.

Suddenly, the tail-lights of the lorry vanish. "Where are they?" asks Bill. "Must have turned off somewhere!" mutters Growler and orders the driver to take the first turning they come to. "It's a farm!" says Rupert. They stop the car and get out, only to find it's a tumbledown old place that's been abandoned for years. "Nobody here!" shrugs Growler. "I'm not so sure of that!" exclaims Rupert and holds up a wisp of wool he's found by the door of the barn.

"Well done, Rupert!" says P.C. Growler. "It seems this farm is not quite so deserted as it looks . . ." The doors of the barn are firmly locked, but as two burly policemen hurl themselves against them they fly open with a tremendous crash and reveal the entire gang, who are gathered round their lorry, unloading sacks of wool as quickly as they can. "Well I never!" gasps Growler. "Look at all those sacks! I think this lot have got some explaining to do . . ."

RUPERT SEES THE THIEVES CAUGHT

Although the thieves are cornered, they
Make one last dash to get away . . .

They've given Growler's men the slip
But something makes the wool thieves trip . . .

"Look!" Rupert cries. "A length of string!
But who could have done such a thing!"

Two Imps of Spring are standing there,
"We stopped the thieves!" the pair declare.

"Run for it lads!" cries one of the crooks. The gang rush towards the open doors of the barn, shoving Growler and the other policemen out of the way. They scramble to their feet and manage to grab one of the thieves, but the others run off as fast as their legs can carry them. Just when it seems they are bound to get away, the men suddenly stumble and go sprawling in a great heap. "W. . .what happened?" asks Rupert. "It looked as though something tripped them up . . ."

P.C. Growler gets his handcuffs out and hurries forward to arrest the thieves. Rupert and Bill follow close behind. When they get nearer, Rupert sees that there is a sort of trip-wire stretched between the gateposts of the old farm. "So that explains it!" he says. "But who . . .?" he breaks off as the sound of shrill laughter comes from behind a nearby bush. Two Imps of Spring step out and show that it was *they* who stopped the thieves . . . using a ball of wool!

"Well done!" says Growler. "But how can
You have known where to find their van?"

"We came here with them, then we hopped
Down from the lorry when it stopped!"

Now Growler's caught the real thieves, he
Says he will set the first Imp free . . .

"But first, there's something I must do . . .
Drive back to Nutwood with these two!"

"Imps of Spring!" marvels Growler. "You did well to stop the thieves like that, but how did you know where they were hiding?" "We came here on top of their lorry!" the Imps reply. "We saw them catch Rupert and were just climbing up to set him free when the lorry started to move! We hopped off as soon as they arrived at the farm, then hid behind these bushes to see what would happen next. We didn't want you to see us at first in case you still thought we stole the wool!"

"Oh, no," laughs Growler. "As soon as Bill told me what was happening, I could see that the farmer had made a mistake. I'm going to set your friend free the moment I get back to Nutwood! Talking of Nutwood . . ." he continues, turning to Rupert and Bill, "it's high time we were *all* getting back there. Your parents must be wondering why you are both out so late!" The pals climb into Growler's car, and after waving farewell to the Imps, are soon speeding home.

RUPERT AND BILL RETURN SAFELY

*It's late, but he describes the pair's
Adventure to the startled Bears.*

*"Wool thieves!" says Mrs. Bear. "Dear me!"
Then brings the chums their bedtime tea.*

*Next morning, Farmer Brown calls round
To give back Rupert's sheep he's found . . .*

*He thanks the pals and says, "Could you
Please give my thanks to the Imps too?"*

P.C. Growler drives the pals to Rupert's house and tells his parents how they have helped to catch a cunning gang of crooks. "I'll telephone Bill's parents and let them know what's happened," says Mr. Bear. "It's so late I think he should stay here for the night." As he makes the call, Mrs. Bear comes back from the kitchen carrying a tray. "I expect you're both hungry after all that excitement," she says. "Time for a quick supper, then off to bed for a good night's sleep."

Next morning the pals are having their breakfast when there is a knock at the door. "It's Farmer Brown!" exclaims Rupert. "I heard all about the wool thieves from P.C. Growler!" the farmer explains. "I've come to say thank you – and to return something I found in one of my fields! Please tell the Imps of Spring I'm sorry I got so cross with them. From now on they will always be welcome to help themselves to as much wool as they can carry!" The End.

These two pictures of Mrs. Bear's kitchen look identical, but there are ten differences between them. Can you spot them all?

44

RUPERT
and the
Sea Urchin

John Harrold.

RUPERT RECEIVES AN INVITATION

One morning Nutwood's postman brings
A note for Rupert when he rings . . .

"Old Captain Binnacle wants me
To stay with his niece by the sea!"

"I'll help you pack," says Mrs. Bear.
"You'll need some spare clothes while you're there."

Soon Rupert's journey has begun.
"Goodbye!" his parents call, "Have fun!"

One morning, at the start of the summer holidays, Rupert hears a knock at the door. He hurries to answer it and finds the village postman, waiting to hand him a letter from his bag. "It's for you," he tells Rupert. "All the way from Rocky Bay . . ." When he opens the letter, Rupert gives a cry of delight and hurries to join his parents. "Captain Binnacle's written," he tells them. "His niece is staying with him and he wants me to come and join them for a few days . . ."

"What a good idea!" says Mrs. Bear. "Let's go and pack a suitcase full of all the things you'll need . . ." While Rupert is busy packing, his father looks up the time of trains to Rocky Bay. "There's one leaving this afternoon," he declares. "I'll send a telegram to let them know you're coming and you can set off as soon as you've had some lunch." Later that day, Rupert's parents take him to the station and wave goodbye as the train starts to leave. "Have fun!" they call.

RUPERT MEETS ROSIE

The Captain's niece tells Rupert she
Has come to meet him. "I'm Rosie!"

"My uncle's cabin's where we'll stay.
Let's go and put your case away . . ."

The pair climb up until they reach
The cabin, high above the beach.

Then, just as they're about to go
Rupert hears Rosie gasp, "Oh, no!"

When Rupert arrives at Rocky Bay he is met at the station by Captain Binnacle's niece. "Hello," she says. "My name's Rosie. My uncle's had to take a group of tourists out round the bay, but he should be back later this afternoon. He asked me to show you the way to his cabin." The pair set off through the cobbled streets of Rocky Bay and Rupert soon recognises the Captain's shack, perched high on a rocky headland. "You can leave your case there, then come and explore," says Rosie.

It's quite a clamber to get to Captain Binnacle's cabin and Rosie leads the way up a steep flight of steps. Inside the shack are two new bunk beds which the Captain has had specially fitted for his visitors, but everything else is exactly as Rupert remembers. There are oil lamps hanging from the ceiling and some nautical-looking charts neatly rolled up on the table. "Come and look at some shells I found . . ." starts Rosie, then she breaks off with a gasp. "Oh, no!"

RUPERT SEES SOMEONE SLEEPING

*"My uncle's nets!" she cries. "Outside –
Look at that big knot someone's tied!"*

*The two friends rush outside and find
A makeshift hammock of some kind . . .*

*"There's somebody inside, I'm sure,"
Says Rupert. "I just heard them snore!"*

*As Rupert gives the net a shake
The sleeping figure starts to wake.*

"What's the matter?" asks Rupert anxiously. "It's my uncle's nets!" says Rosie, peering out of the window at the line where Captain Binnacle hangs his nets to dry in the sun. "They were all neat and tidy this morning, but now look what's happened. Somebody has tied them in a big knot!" They hurry outside to take a closer look at the nets. "That's strange," murmurs Rupert. "It almost looks as though someone has been using them as a makeshift hammock."

"It *is* a hammock!" cries Rosie as the pair move closer towards the tangle of nets. "I wonder who can have made it?" "Listen," says Rupert. "I can hear someone snoring. There's somebody inside the hammock, and they're still fast asleep!" "Who can it be?" whispers Rosie. "I don't know," answers Rupert. "There's only one way to find out!" He reaches out and shakes the hammock gently. Nothing happens. He shakes the hammock again. This time the sleeping figure begins to stir . . .

RUPERT WAKES A STRANGER

It's someone Rupert's never seen –
An Imp-like creature, dressed in green.

The stranger yawns, then turns to glare
Quite crossly at the startled pair.

"Who are you?" Rupert asks. "And when
Will you sort out these nets again?"

"I won't!" he laughs. "That's how they'll stay!"
Then shakes his fist and runs away.

The sleeping figure wakes with a start. It sits up in the hammock and looks about warily. Rupert and Rosie have never seen anything like it. The creature they've woken looks a little like an Elf or an Imp, but it is dressed in a scaly green costume and has a strange, spiky shell as a hat. As soon as it catches sight of Rupert and Rosie it jumps out of the hammock and stands glaring at them suspiciously. "Who are you?" asks Rosie. "And what have you done to my uncle's nets?"

"Shan't tell you my name!" answers the stranger defiantly. "I wasn't doing any harm! These nets make a perfect hammock!" "But what about Captain Binnacle?" asks Rupert. "He'll be cross when he sees what a mess you've made." "What do I care?" shrugs the creature, turning to leave. "Perhaps he should use them as a hammock all the time!" "Come back!" calls Rupert, but the mischievous stranger runs off, kicking over a pile of lobster pots as he goes . . .

RUPERT TELLS CAPTAIN BINNACLE

*Down by the water's edge, the pair
See that he's got a small boat there.*

*Before Rupert can catch him, he
Hops in and paddles out to sea.*

*The Captain is surprised to find
The mess that has been left behind . . .*

*He thinks perhaps the creature might
Have been some sort of young Sea Sprite.*

The stranger runs off down some steps and hurries out along the slipway. Rupert and Rosie arrive just in time to see him pulling a curious little boat towards the water's edge. He launches it quickly, hops aboard and paddles out to sea. "Stop!" calls Rupert, but the boat speeds out round the headland and is soon lost to view. "What a horrid little creature!" says Rosie. "Who do you think he was and why did he come ashore at Rocky Bay?"

Rupert and Rosie return to the cabin and find Captain Binnacle staring at the tangle of nets. When he learns what has happened, he looks very thoughtful and asks Rupert to tell him exactly what the stranger looked like. "Sounds like some sort of Sea Sprite to me," he declares. "Folk say they don't exist, but I know better. Plenty of strange creatures live in the sea. Sprites don't normally come ashore though. That's why they're hardly ever seen . . ."

RUPERT LISTENS TO THE MERBOY

Next morning it's a perfect day
To go exploring Rocky Bay.

But soon the pair are sure they hear
A friendly call from somewhere near . . .

"The Merboy!" Rupert cries as he
Shows Rosie his friend from the sea.

The Merboy asks the pals if they
Have seen a Sprite who's run away . . .

Next morning, Rupert and Rosie wake up early and decide to go and explore the rock pools down by the beach. "I wonder if that spiky Sprite creature will be there again," says Rosie. When they reach the beach they can see no sign of him and are soon happily exploring a deep pool. Suddenly Rupert hears somebody call his name and looks up with a start. "It's the Merboy!" he cries. "Who?" asks Rosie. "The Merboy!" says Rupert. "Look, there he is, waving to us from the sea."

Rupert has met the Merboy before. He knows that he serves King Neptune and lives in his palace under the sea. "This is Rosie . . ." he starts to say. "I know!" smiles the Merboy. "She's Captain Binnacle's niece. It's my job to know everyone who comes to Rocky Bay." "Then you must know the spiky little creature we found asleep in Captain Binnacle's nets," says Rupert. "Oh dear," the Merboy sighs. "That sounds like the Sea Urchin. He's always up to some sort of mischief!"

*"Please summon me with this shell when
The Sea Urchin appears again."*

*The pair agree to search the shore
In case the Sprite's come back once more . . .*

*They clamber round the headland where
He vanished – could he still be there?*

*"He must have dropped this!" Rosie cries
And points to where a paddle lies.*

The Merboy explains that the Urchin is a young Sea Sprite who has run away from school. "King Neptune's given *me* the task of finding him and making him come back!" he groans. "You couldn't help me, could you?" he asks. "All you have to do is blow this shell the moment you see him again. If you two could keep an eye on the shore, I'd be free to get on with searching the sea!" Rupert agrees to help and the Merboy swims off, leaving him and Rosie to carry on exploring . . .

Rupert and Rosie walk to the headland where they last saw the Sea Urchin. It's a steep clamber up on to the rocks and along a narrow path, but they eventually find themselves in thc next bay, which seems to be completely deserted. "It doesn't look as if he has been back," says Rupert, but just as he turns to go, Rosie gives a sudden cry and points to something lying on the sand. "The Urchin's paddle!" she exclaims. "It looks as if it's been washed up by the tiide . . ."

RUPERT PLANS A RESCUE

*Then, by the water's edge, they see
The Urchin's boat – but where is he?*

*"Help!" comes a sudden cry of fear.
"The tide's come in. I'm stranded here!"*

*"Quick, Rosie! This way," Rupert cries,
"To where your uncle's dinghy lies . . ."*

*Rupert and Rosie take an oar
Then row out swiftly from the shore.*

Worried at finding the paddle, but no sign of the Sea Urchin, Rupert and Rosie decide to search the shore. Suddenly they see a familiar boat, lying abandoned at the water's edge. "What's happened?" asks Rosie, as they hurry forward to take a closer look. "Look!" answers Rupert and points to the Sea Urchin, who is stranded on the tip of a rock, surrounded by water. "Help!" he calls to the friends. "Please help me. I'm stuck here. The tide's coming in and I can't swim!"

There is only one way that Rupert and Rosie can reach the Urchin in time. "Come on!" calls Rupert. "We'll have to take your uncle's boat and row out to the rock!" The pair hurry back to the spot below Captain Binnacle's cabin where the boat is moored. Untying the mooring rope from a metal ring, they push the boat down to the water's edge and climb aboard. Then, taking an oar each, they row as hard as they can towards the rock where the Sea Urchin is stranded.

RUPERT HEARS THE URCHIN'S TALE

*They reach the Urchin's rock and tell
Him to climb in the boat as well.*

*"You're safe now," Rosie smiles as they
Row back towards the sandy bay.*

*The Urchin tells how his mishap
All started with a little nap . . .*

*"The tide came in and stranded me –
I don't know how to swim, you see!"*

Rupert and Rosie steer the rowing boat as near to the rock as they can. They stop rowing and drift in closer until Rupert is able to reach out and hold the boat steady. "Climb aboard!" he tells the overjoyed Urchin. "Thank goodness you found me!" the Urchin cries. "I don't know *what* would have happened if you hadn't come along. The tide was getting higher and higher . . ." "You're safe now," says Rosie reassuringly as the little boat glides towards the beach.

Rupert pulls the boat ashore while the Sea Urchin tells the two friends how he came to be stranded on the rock. "I came back to Rocky Bay to explore the rest of the coast and found a little island which looked the perfect place to have a rest. The sun was so warm that I fell asleep. When I woke up, I discovered that the tide had come in and carried off my boat! I didn't know what to do because I can't swim. We had lessons at school but I never paid any attention . . ."

RUPERT ROUSES A SEA SERPENT

"We need to summon help, but how?"
Thinks Rupert. "I'll blow the shell now!"

A serpent pops up angrily.
"What's this?" he cries. "Who's calling me?"

The serpent smiles. "Why, bless me! You're
Young Rupert Bear! We've met before . . ."

He scolds the Urchin, then says he
Will take him home, across the sea.

After being stranded on the rock for so long, the Urchin tells Rupert he is much too tired to paddle all the way home. Rupert thinks hard for a moment, then remembers the shell the Merboy gave him to summon help if he saw the Urchin again. He blows into the shell as hard as he can and a long, loud note sounds out across the bay. At first nothing happens, but then, suddenly, there is a tremendous splash as up pops an angry-looking Sea-Serpent . . .

"What's this?" cries the Serpent. "Who woke me up by blowing that noisy trumpet? Why, it's Rupert!" he smiles. "And this must be Captain Binnacle's niece, little Rosie." The Serpent's smile fades when he catches sight of the wretched Urchin. "You!" he snorts. "The naughtiest Sprite in the sea! The Merboy told me you'd been up to your tricks again. Climb on to my back and I'll take you home. You can tell King Neptune what you mean by running away from school!"

RUPERT AND ROSIE RETURN

The serpent swims off with the Sprite
Perched on his back, "Just hold on tight!"

Back on the beach, the two chums find
The Urchin's left his boat behind . . .

The pair decide to take it back
And hurry to the Captain's shack.

The Captain's pleased, but says that they
Must sort the nets out the next day.

"Hold on tight!" the serpent tells the Urchin and starts to swim swiftly out to sea. "Goodbye!" calls Rosie. "I hope King Neptune isn't too hard on him," she tells Rupert. "So do I," he answers. "I'm sure the Sea Urchin isn't really as bad as he seems . . ." They wander back to the cove where they left their bucket and net and see the Urchin's boat and paddle, still lying on the sand. "We'd better not leave them here," says Rupert. "Let's take them with us for safe keeping . . ."

As Rupert and Rosie near the cabin, Captain Binnacle comes hurrying out to meet them. He smiles when he sees the little boat which Rupert is carrying. "That's a Sea-Sprite's," he says. "I'd recognise it anywhere!" Rupert tells him all about their adventure and how they had to rescue the Urchin from a rock. "I'm glad he's safe," says the Captain, "but what about my nets?" "Don't worry!" says Rupert. "Rosie and I will sort everything out tomorrow."

RUPERT MEETS THE URCHIN AGAIN

Next morning, Rupert wakes to see
The nets are hung out tidily . . .

Outside, he finds the Urchin, who
Has stacked the lobster pots up too!

"I've come back to tell everyone
I'm sorry for the things I've done."

Then, down below, the two friends see
The Merboy waving eagerly.

Next morning Rupert wakes up early and looks out of the window of Captain Binnacle's cabin. To his amazement, he sees that the nets, which were in such a tangle the night before, are hanging neatly on the line, and that the lobster pots have been tidied up carefully. He hurries outside to see what's happened and is just in time to see the Sea Urchin stacking the last of the lobster pots on top of all the others. "So you came back to help us!" exclaims Rupert.

"I'm sorry I made such a mess," the Urchin tells Rupert, as Rosie comes out to see what's going on. "The fact is, I don't *mean* to cause any mischief but everything at school is so boring that I have to get out and explore from time to time. I love to come ashore at places like Rocky Bay, but, because I'm a Sea-sprite, I'm not really meant to . . ." As he speaks there is a call from the rocks below. Rupert and Rosie peer down and see that it's the Merboy . . .

RUPERT AND ROSIE WAVE GOODBYE

*"King Neptune says the Urchin may
Start working with me straightaway!"*

*"The first thing that I'll do for him
Is make sure he knows how to swim!"*

*"Good luck!" Rupert and Rosie cry
As they wave their new friend goodbye.*

*The Captain smiles and says that he
Is glad things ended happily!*

The Merboy tells Rupert and Rosie to bring the runaway Urchin down to the water's edge. "I've got some important news to tell you all," he declares. "It seems that King Neptune has heard all about the Urchin's adventures and decided that the best thing he can do is to leave school and become an apprentice straightaway. The first thing I'm going to do is to teach you how to swim!" laughs the Merboy, as the delighted young Sprite gets ready to paddle home in his little boat.

"Good luck!" call Rupert and Rosie as they wave goodbye to the little Urchin and watch him set off across the bay, together with the Merboy. When they go back and tell Captain Binnacle what's happened, he seems glad to hear that King Neptune decided to let the mischievous Sprite off so lightly, "After all," he chuckles, "*I* ran away to sea once, you know! Can't say I blame a young Sprite for wanting to see what things are like, here on dry land . . ." The End.

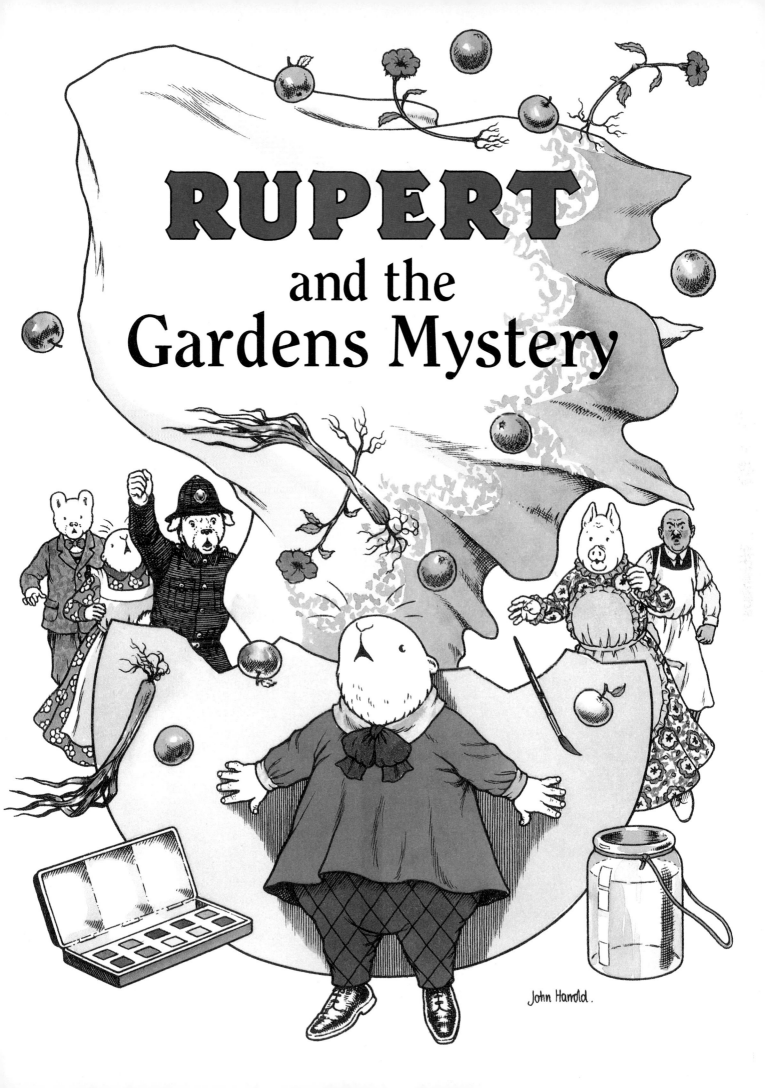

RUPERT
and the
Gardens Mystery

John Harrold.

RUPERT IS ASTONISHED

One sunny morning, Rupert spies
A sight that makes him rub his eyes . . .

"Whatever can the matter be?"
His father asks him. "Come and see!"

Out in the garden, it seems that
Someone has crushed the spring bulbs flat . . .

"Look!" Rupert cries. "I think I've found
A mark that's been left on the ground . . ."

One morning, just before Easter, Rupert is woken by a shaft of golden light, streaming into his room. "It's going to be a sunny day," he thinks and throws open the window. As he looks out, he gives a cry of astonishment and hurries off to wake his parents. "W. .what's the matter?" blinks Mr. Bear as he pulls on his dressing gown and stumbles out on to the landing. "It's the garden," Rupert cries. "Something terrible's happened. Come and see . . ."

Following Rupert into the garden, Mr. Bear soon sees why his son was so surprised . . . All the spring bulbs, that looked so wonderful the day before, have been trampled into the ground, as if someone has been marching about in the flower beds! "Who can have done such a thing?" he gasps. "I don't know," says Rupert. "I didn't hear anything during the night . . ." Then he breaks off and points to something he's spotted in one of the flower beds.

RUPERT FINDS A CLUE

"A footprint! But who left it there?
It seems so odd!" gasps Mr. Bear.

"Come on!" he says. "We'd better go
And let Constable Growler know."

The Constable is puzzled too –
He doesn't quite know what to do . . .

Then Mrs. Pig appears. Can she
See Growler very urgently?

"Good gracious!" gasps Mr. Bear as he looks at what Rupert has found. "It's a footprint of some sort, although I can't imagine what kind of creature made it!" "Whatever it was must have crushed all the flowers," says Rupert. "That's right!" murmurs Mr. Bear. "I don't like the look of this at all! Come on, Rupert. We'll get dressed, then tell Constable Growler what's happened. If this creature's as big as it seems, then it could be dangerous . . ."

P.C. Growler is as puzzled by the strange footprints as Rupert and his father. "Never seen anything like this before . . ." he mutters. "I wonder if it could be those Fox brothers up to one of their silly pranks?" "Surely they wouldn't have trampled all over our flowers?" says Mr. Bear. "That would be too much, even for them!" Before Growler can reply a voice calls his name and Mrs. Pig appears at the garden gate. "Thank goodness I've found you," she cries.

RUPERT HEARS MRS. PIG'S TALE

"My daffodils were trampled flat,"
She starts to tell him, "just like that . . ."

"Our garden shed was ransacked too!
That's why I came to look for you . . ."

"Thieves!" Growler cries. But no, she found
A monster's footprint on the ground!

Her tale is interrupted when
Young Gregory arrives just then . . .

"What's wrong?" asks P.C. Growler. "It's my garden," declares Podgy's mother. "When I woke up this morning all the daffodils in my flower bed had been trampled to the ground . . .just like these!" "Dear me!" exclaims the policeman. "I don't suppose you saw any sign of what did it?" "No," replies Mrs. Pig. "But the door of our garden shed was left wide open, with everything strewn all over the lawn . . ." "Thieves, eh?" says Growler and reaches for his notebook.

"Oh, no!" cries Podgy's mother. "You don't understand. It wasn't thieves who trampled down the daffodils: it was some sort of terrible monster. We found a giant footprint in the corner of the flower bed . . ." "So did we!" says Mr. Bear. "Rupert found it, next to the trampled bulbs . . ." At that moment, Gregory Guineapig comes running into the garden. "Constable Growler!" he calls. "My mother sent me to find you. Something dreadful's happened!"

RUPERT LISTENS TO MRS. GUINEA PIG

His mother's had a dreadful fright
"Our garden's been wrecked in the night!"

"My table cloth's been stolen too,
I dread to think by what or who!"

"The Monster!" Rupert cries. "I'm sure
We'll find that it has struck once more!"

"Don't worry!" Growler says, "I'll go
And find out what my colleagues know . . ."

"It's something to do with your garden, isn't it?" asks Rupert. "Yes," gasps Gregory. "But how did you know?" Rupert has just started to explain about the mysterious trail of footprints when Mrs. Guineapig arrives in a terrible tizzy. Something has trampled all over her prize tulips . . ."That's not all!" she adds as the others listen attentively. "Whatever it was pulled down my washing line and made off with my best linen table cloth!"

P.C.Growler doesn't know what to make of such strange goings on! "It must be the same creature," says Rupert. "It's footprints were found in all three gardens . . ." "I know!" groans the policeman. "But I've got no idea what sort of animal we're looking for. Trampled bulbs, ransacked sheds, and now . . .missing table cloths! It's all very peculiar. I think I'd better telephone my colleagues in Nutchester." he declares. "Perhaps they'll know something about it . . ."

RUPERT SPOTS THE 'MONSTER'

Soon afterwards the Bears all hear
A whistling sound from somewhere near . . .

They hurry to the gate and see
As strange a sight as there could be . . .

A hidden creature of some kind
Runs past, with Growler close behind!

He orders it to stop, but on
The creature runs, until it's gone.

Deciding that there's nothing more to be done, Gregory and his mother make their way home, together with Mrs. Pig. "I still can't imagine what sort of creature trampled all over our flowers!" says Rupert's mother. Suddenly, a shrill whistling sound fills the air. "That's Constable Growler's police whistle!" cries Rupert. "It sounds as if he's coming this way . . ." He runs to the garden gate, together with his parents, then gives a startled cry . . .

"Look!" exclaims Rupert. "Good gracious!" cries Mr. Bear, "Whatever's that?" Speeding towards the cottage comes P.C.Growler, in hot pursuit of a strange, tall creature, wrapped in some sort of sheet. "Stop!" cries Growler, but the hidden creature runs on with giant strides and vanishes off across the common. "It's no use!" puffs the exhausted policeman, stopping to take off his helmet and mop his brow. "It's just too fast for me to catch!"

RUPERT'S MOTHER HELPS GROWLER

*"I chased it from the high street, where
It upset everybody there . . ."*

*"Good gracious!" Rupert's mother cries,
"That cloth is one I recognise!"*

*"The missing cloth?" gasps Growler. "Then
That was our 'Monster' once again!"*

*"It might be dangerous! I'll go
And let the Nutchester men know . . ."*

"W..what were you chasing?" Rupert asks Growler. "I don't really know!" shrugs the policeman. "I was on my way back to the station, when I suddenly heard a cry of alarm. As soon as I reached the high street I saw that . . that *thing* bump into poor Mr. Anteater, then knock over the whole of the greengrocer's display. That's when I blew my whistle and started to give chase . . ." "It . . it was wrapped in Mrs. Guineapig's table cloth!" declares Mrs. Bear.

"Are you sure that was Mrs. Guineapig's cloth?" asks P.C. Growler. "Yes," says Rupert's mother. "I'd recognise it anywhere . . ." "Then this must be the creature that wrecked everyone's gardens!" the policeman declares. "But why should it hide under a table cloth?" asks Mr. Bear. "I don't know," says Growler. "Perhaps as a disguise? Whatever the creature is, it could be dangerous. I want everyone to keep away from the common, while I go and telephone Nutchester."

RUPERT FOLLOWS GREGORY

*Rupert decides to go and tell
Young Gregory the news as well.*

*"Can't stop!" his chum declares. "You see,
I've got my painting things with me . . ."*

*"How strange!" thinks Rupert. "I'm quite sure
That Gregory can't even draw!"*

*He follows Gregory to find
Just what his chum has got in mind.*

After Growler has left, Rupert decides to go and tell Gregory all about the mysterious creature. Avoiding the common, he takes the long way round to his chum's house and spots the little guineapig, going out for a walk. "Wait for me!" he calls. To Rupert's surprise, Gregory is carrying a paintbox and a jar of water. "I . . I'm on my way to do some sketching," he declares and hurries off without another word. "How strange," thinks Rupert. "I didn't know Gregory liked painting."

"I wonder what he's going to paint?" thinks Rupert as he watches Gregory hurry away. He's certainly carrying a paint box and a pot of water, but where's his sketchbook?" Overcome with curiosity, Rupert decides to follow his chum to find out what he's up to. At first nothing unusual happens, then Gregory stops and peers all round. From his hiding place behind an old tree, Rupert sees him turn off the main path and disappear up a narrow farm track . . .

RUPERT LEARNS GREGORY'S SECRET

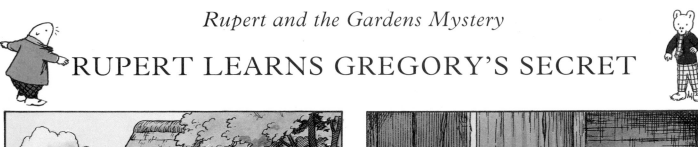

*"A ruined barn! But why was he
So keen to come here secretly?"*

*As Rupert peers around the door
His pal lifts something from the straw . . .*

*"A huge egg!" Rupert gasps, but he
Is overheard by Gregory.*

*"What egg?" he cries, attempting to
Keep it well-hidden, out of view.*

Following Gregory up the narrow track, Rupert finds that it leads to an enormous ruined barn. He is just in time to see his friend prise open the barn doors and slip inside . . . "I wonder why he's being so secretive?" thinks Rupert and tip-toes up the path to take a closer look. As he peers round the open door, he spots Gregory, rummaging about in a heap of straw. "Good!" he cries. "It's still here." To Rupert's amazement he pulls out a huge egg . . .

Unaware that Rupert is watching, Gregory rests the egg on top of an old packing crate then turns to open his paints. "I say," cries Rupert, "that's the biggest egg I've ever seen!" "Who? What!" squeaks Gregory. "Oh, it's you, Rupert. Fancy creeping up on me like that!" "I'm sorry," says Rupert. "I only wanted to see what you were painting. Wherever did you get that enormous egg?" "What egg?" says Gregory, standing in front of the box.

RUPERT SEES THE EGG MOVE

At last he explains how he found
The huge egg lying on the ground . . .

"I want to paint it straightaway
To show you all on Easter Day!"

"But Gregory, it must belong
To someone. Taking it is wrong!"

As Rupert speaks, the two pals see
The egg start moving suddenly . . .

"Don't be silly!" says Rupert. "I saw the egg when you took it from under the straw . . ." "You can't have it!" cries Gregory. "I found it. It was lying in our vegetable patch!" "I don't want to take it," laughs Rupert. "I only want to have a closer look." "Oh, all right," says Gregory. "But it's meant to be a surprise. I'm going to paint it bright colours and have the biggest Easter egg in Nutwood. You won't tell any of the others, will you?"

"Of course not," says Rupert. "but where did the egg come from?" "I just told you," says Gregory. "Yes," says Rupert. "But what sort of creature could have left it there in the first place? It won't be very happy it it comes back and finds the egg's gone. If I were you, I'd put it back straightaway." "Shan't!" squeaks Gregory. "It's my egg now, and I'm going to paint it." Just then, the pals hear a strange tapping sound as the egg begins to move . . .

RUPERT TAKES THE EGG BACK

Gregory tries to run away,
But Rupert says they've got to stay.

"Before the egg begins to crack
Let's see if we can put it back."

He carries the egg nervously
What will the baby creature be?

As they arrive, the startled pair
Are shocked to see what's standing there . . .

"Help!" cries Gregory and runs towards the door. "Come back!" says Rupert. "We can't just go off and leave the egg to hatch out in an empty barn. Whatever's inside will be frightened and need help . . ." "But it could be anything!" cries Gregory, nervously. "Come on," says Rupert, picking up the egg as gently as he can. "Show me the exact spot in your garden where you found the egg and we'll put it back there to hatch out safely . . ."

On the way back to Gregory's house, Rupert hears the tapping grow louder and starts to think of all the things that might have laid such an enormous egg . . . It can't have been an ordinary bird, so perhaps it was an alligator, or a giant snake, or even a fire-breathing dragon . . . "We're nearly there now," says Gregory, breaking in on Rupert's thoughts. The pair turn into Gregory's garden but have only gone a few paces when they stop and stare at what lies ahead.

RUPERT SEES THE 'MONSTER' AGAIN

The Monster's back, and seems to be
Searching the garden thoroughly . . .

Replacing the egg carefully,
The two pals turn around and flee!

The pair keep running until they
Are certain that they've got away.

As Growler sees them run along
He stops and asks the chums, "What's wrong?"

There, in the middle of the Guineapigs' vegetable patch, stands the same strange creature which P.C.Growler chased through the middle of Nutwood earlier that morning. "It's come back!" gasps Gregory, "Only this time it's trampling our vegetables . . ." "Quick!" whispers Rupert. "I don't think it's noticed us yet." Putting the egg down on the soft grass, he grabs Gregory's hand and marches him back along the garden path before the creature looks up.

The moment they are clear of the garden, Rupert and Gregory take to their heels and run to fetch help as fast as they can. "W . . what if it follows us?" wails Gregory. "Don't worry," says Rupert. "I'm sure it was too busy with the vegetable patch to have seen us . . ." As they race round the corner, the pair are relieved to see P.C. Growler, strolling towards them. "Hello," he smiles. "You two seem in a bit of a rush. Whatever's the matter?"

RUPERT AND GROWLER ARE SURPRISED

*"The 'Monster'!" Rupert gasps. "We saw
It trampling down more plants, I'm sure . . ."*

*"I'll deal with this!" says Growler. "Though
You'll need to show me where to go . . ."*

*"I've asked an expert from the zoo
To come and tell us what to do."*

*"Look!" Growler cries out in surprise,
Unable to believe his eyes . . .*

At first Rupert is too out of breath to say anything more than, "The . . .the monster! It's come back . . ." "Monster?" asks Growler. "You mean the thing I chased along the high street?" "That's right." nods Gregory. "It's in our garden again, trampling on the vegetables!" "This calls for firm measures!" says Growler, producing his truncheon. He tells Gregory to go and wait at the police station, while Rupert shows him where the creature's lurking . . .

On the way to Gregory's garden, Growler tells Rupert the police in Nutchester have promised to send someone from the local zoo to look at the mysterious footprints. "I don't suppose you saw what the creature was?" he adds hopefully. "No," says Rupert. "It was still covered by the tablecloth." "Not a sound!" whispers the policeman as they near the garden gate. "We'll try to creep up on it." The pair peep cautiously into the garden, then reel back in surprise . . .

"An ostrich!" he gasps. "And I see
It's laid an egg as well. Bless me!"

Then, as the startled pair draw near,
They see an ostrich chick appear!

The mother ostrich spots the pair
And fixes Growler with a stare . . .

"Don't move!" warns Rupert, but too late –
She starts to charge towards the gate!

"An ostrich!" gasps Rupert. "Look! It's all tangled up in Mrs. Guineapig's tablecloth." "So that's the mystery creature!" cries Growler. "No wonder its footprints looked so strange . . ." The huge bird pays no attention to the newcomers, but peers attentively at the egg, which Rupert left lying by the side of the path. The tapping sound from inside the egg grows louder and louder, until, suddenly, the shell cracks and out pops a tiny ostrich chick . . .

"I hope the zoo chappie gets here soon!" says P.C.Growler. "I'm not sure I fancy trying to take these two into custody." As he speaks, the mother ostrich looks up and glares at him crossly. "Don't make any sudden moves!" warns Rupert, but it's too late. Stepping forward, to place herself between her chick and the strangers, the ostrich flaps her wings then charges up the path. "Watch out!" cries Growler. "She's coming this way . . ."

RUPERT MEETS A ZOO KEEPER

The pair retreat, but as they do
They spot a lorry from the zoo.

The keeper goes across to say
Hello to Olive straightaway . . .

"A baby ostrich! Goodness me!"
He smiles and strokes it tenderly.

He hands Rupert the chick and then
Says, "Time we got you home again."

As Rupert and Growler back away from the angry ostrich, they hear a lorry coming along the road towards them. It stops and a man in a zoo-keeper's uniform hops down from the cab. "They said in the village I'd catch you here," he smiles. "Looks like I'm just in time!" Walking towards the ostrich, he raises his cap and greets her like a long lost friend. "Hello, Olive," he calls. "No need to get excited. I'm sure these two gentlemen don't mean any harm . . ."

"Well, I never!" smiles the keeper as he spots the ostrich chick in Gregory's garden. "What a splendid little fellow. You must be very proud." The mother ostrich seems quite content as he picks up the chick and hands it to Rupert to hold. "We'll take you both home now," the keeper adds gently. "You can ride in the back of the lorry, while young Rupert here looks after your chick." The ostrich smiles approvingly and follows him back to the van.

RUPERT GOES TO THE ZOO

*"Goodbye!" waves Growler, glad to see
That things have ended happily.*

*"It's just as well the 'Monster' you
Discovered had come from our zoo!"*

*"The reason Olive had to stay
Was someone took her egg away . . ."*

*Then, as a set of gates appear
The keeper says, "We're getting near!"*

When everything is ready, and Olive is safely aboard, the zoo keeper drives off, leaving P.C. Growler to go and tell Gregory it's all right to come home. "I thought it might be Olive the moment I heard about your mysterious footprints," the keeper tells Rupert. "She went missing from the zoo a couple of days ago and nobody knew where she'd gone . . ." "Why did she run away?" asks Rupert. "And why ever did she make such a mess of everyone's gardens?"

"Olive probably got a bit bored," explains the keeper. "I wouldn't be surprised if she simply wanted to see more of the outside world . . .The thing that puzzles me is why she spent so long searching all those gardens. It's almost as if someone took her egg and hid it somewhere where she couldn't find it!" Rupert says nothing but thinks of Gregory and the ruined barn . . . "Never mind!" says the keeper as they near the zoo. "She's almost home now . . ."

RUPERT SEES OLIVE'S HOUSE

Inside the zoo, Rupert can see
The animals all wander free . . .

They stop outside a tall hut where
The ostrich lives – "She likes it there . . ."

They wave goodbye to Olive, then
Drive back to Nutwood once again . . .

"My Easter egg!" sighs Gregory.
"The biggest one I'll ever see . . ."

Inside the zoo gates, Rupert is amazed to find a large park, full of lots of different animals, all roaming as they please. "No bars and cages here!" smiles the keeper. "Look! There's Olive's house." He stops the lorry outside a tall hut with a thatched roof. The ostrich seems delighted to be home, and soon leads her little chick inside. "Talking of homes, it's time you were getting back to Nutwood," the keeper tells Rupert. "Come on, I'll take you there."

When the zoo keeper arrives in Nutwood, he drives straight to Mrs. Guineapig's house to apologise for what happened to her table cloth. "Don't worry!" she says. "I'm only sorry that poor ostrich got so badly tangled up in it . . ." "I don't suppose you've got any more big eggs?" asks Gregory, picking up a piece of the broken shell. "I'm afraid not," smiles the keeper. "Just as well!" laughs Rupert. "Who knows what might hatch out next?" The End.

RUPERT and

One winter morning Rupert's told
To wrap up well against the cold.

Something strange has happened to the Nutwood weather. Although there are only a few days left before Christmas, it still seems very mild. "Never mind, Rupert," says Mrs. Bear. "You should still wrap up well before you go out. If the weather changes, you could get caught in a snowstorm!" "There's not much danger of that," smiles Mr. Bear. "The barometer says we'll have fine weather for the rest of the week . . ."

the **Missing Snow**

*"The weather's mild, but even so
This time of year, there could be snow!"*

*Soon Rupert spots his best pals, who
Are all wrapped up in thick coats too . . .*

All Rupert's friends are wearing their winter coats too. "Phew!" gasps Algy. "It's jolly hot to be wrapped up like this!" "I do hope it snows soon!" says Willie Mouse. "I've written asking Santa for a pair of skis!" "I've asked for some ice skates," says Bill. "They won't be much use if the lake doesn't freeze!" "I asked for a sledge," adds Rupert. "Unless it snows, I won't be able to use that either . . ."

*The chums explain the reasons they
Hope that it snows by Christmas Day.*

"The weather forecast's very strange,"
Says Mr. Bear. "It says 'No change'!"

That evening Rupert wakes to hear
A tapping sound from somewhere near . . .

It's Santa's Little Cowboy who
Says, "Rupert! I've been sent for you . . ."

As soon as Rupert's ready he
Runs to the plane. "Quick, follow me!"

When Rupert goes home for tea that afternoon, he tells his parents how disappointed his pals will be if the weather doesn't get colder. "It's certainly very odd!" says Mr. Bear. "The forecast still says 'fine'. If anything, it seems to be getting even milder . . ." In the evening, when Rupert goes to bed, he lies awake and thinks how dull Christmas will be if it doesn't snow at all. He is just drifting off to sleep when he suddenly hears someone tapping at the window . . .

Opening the window and peering out, Rupert is surprised to see his friend, the Little Cowboy. "Sorry to wake you," he whispers. "Santa's sent me to ask if you can join us at once . . ." "Of course!" says Rupert. "But what's the matter?" "No time to explain!" says the Cowboy. "He'll tell you himself as soon as we arrive . . ." Slipping quietly out of the house, Rupert follows the Cowboy to the edge of the common. "This way!" he calls and points to his plane.

RUPERT VISITS SANTA'S CASTLE

The pair take off and quickly fly
To Santa's castle in the sky.

The Little Cowboy leads the way
To Santa Claus without delay.

It's warm in Santa's office too –
"This winter sun will never do!"

"I need someone like you to go
And ask the Weather Clerk for snow."

Rupert climbs aboard the little plane and is soon flying north through the night sky. "That's where we're heading for!" calls the Cowboy, and points to a cloud that seems to glow on the horizon. As the plane gets nearer, Rupert sees the towers of a castle, bathed in dazzling light. The Cowboy lands in the castle courtyard and hurries to the main gate. "Special visitor for Santa!" he tells the sentries. "Come on, Rupert. I'll take you to see him straightaway . . ."

The Little Cowboy leads the way to Santa's office and knocks at the door. "Come in!" calls a loud voice. "Ah, Rupert! Just the person I wanted to see . . ." Mopping his brow with a handkerchief, Santa explains that he's worried about the mild weather. "Unless it snows soon, lots of children will be disappointed!" he declares. "I must get the Clerk of the Weather to find out what's wrong, but I'm too busy to go and see him. Perhaps you can go instead?"

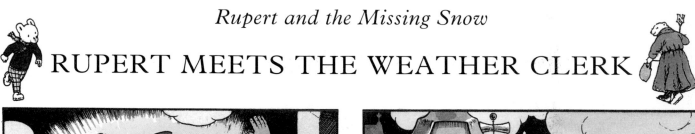

RUPERT MEETS THE WEATHER CLERK

Rupert agrees to help and then
Takes off into the sky again.

"The weather station!" Rupert cries.
"And there's someone I recognise . . ."

The Clerk and his Assistant hear
How there has been no snow this year.

The Clerk takes down a weighty book –
"I'm sure I sent some snow. Yes, look!"

Rupert agrees to do as Santa asks, and follows the Little Cowboy back to his plane. They take off and are soon flying through a dark, star-spangled sky. Just as Rupert is wondering how they will ever find the way, he sees a pale silver light in the distance. "Weather Station ahead!" calls the Cowboy. The plane gets nearer and Rupert can see someone waving. "It's the Weather Clerk's Assistant!" he cries. "He must have seen your plane and come to meet us . . ."

As soon as Rupert explains what's wrong, the Assistant summons his master. "No snow?" says the Clerk. "But I'm sure we sent some!" He hurries inside and pulls down a huge ledger. "There! Snow for Nutwood. Sent from the North Pole last week!" "The North Pole?" asks Rupert. "Yes," the Assistant explains. "Snow clouds are stored there. It acts as a magnet and keeps them safe until they're needed." "Don't worry!" says the Clerk. "I'll send more snow immediately . . ."

RUPERT IS DISAPPOINTED

As Rupert flies back home he's sure
That it will snow, the Clerk's sent more.

On Christmas Eve he waits all day
But there's no sign snow's on the way . . .

Next morning, Rupert wakes to see
There's still no snow. Where can it be?

Rupert unwraps his sledge to find
A note that Santa's left behind.

"Let's hope the snow *arrives* this time!" says the Little Cowboy as they fly back from the Weather Station. It has started to grow light by the time they reach Nutwood and Rupert has to hurry to be sure of getting home before anyone is awake. All day long he keeps looking out of the window but, as evening falls and he helps to finish decorating the Christmas tree, there is *still* no sign of snow. "How odd," he thinks. "The Clerk promised to send some straightaway!"

When Rupert wakes on Christmas Day, he leaps out of bed and hurries to draw the curtains. "Oh, no!" he cries, as he peers out of the window. "It hasn't snowed at all . . ." At the foot of his bed is a large, bulky parcel, which turns out to be a new sledge. Tucked inside the wrapping paper, Rupert finds a note from Santa: "Missing snow more serious than first suspected. Need your help urgently. Little Cowboy will meet you by edge of common. Wear warm clothes . . ."

RUPERT JOINS AN EXPEDITION

He hurries to the common where
The Clerk's Assistant's waiting there . . .

"We have to find the missing snow,"
He says to Rupert as they go.

"The North Pole's where the snow should be,
We store it there in clouds, you see!"

"That's odd! My compass says that we're
At the North Pole, but nothing's here!"

The moment breakfast is over, Rupert puts on his coat and runs to the common. Waiting there are the Little Cowboy and the Weather Clerk's Assistant. "Something's wrong with the weather controls!" the Assistant says. "Hop aboard and I'll tell you all about it . . ." As the plane leaves Nutwood, he explains how the extra snow clouds he sent to the North Pole were mysteriously blown off course. "That's where we're going now," he adds. "To find out what happened . . ."

On and on the little plane flies, further and further north. The air grows cold and frosty. "Look!" cries Rupert as he spots icebergs floating in the water below. "Right on course!" declares the Assistant and begins to direct the Cowboy towards the Pole. After a while, he stops giving directions and peers anxiously at his compass. "I don't understand!" he tells Rupert. "According to my map, we should have reached the Pole, but all I can see is ice and snow!"

RUPERT MEETS HIS UNCLE POLAR

"My Uncle Polar!" Rupert cries.
"He's bound to know where the Pole lies!"

"Look! There's his house. Let's go and see.
I'm sure that he'll remember me . . ."

His two companions come as well
As Rupert goes to ring the bell.

A polar bear appears. "Bless me!"
"Is that my nephew that I see?"

"Let's go back and try again," suggest the Little Cowboy. "No," says the Assistant. "There's nothing there. I'm sure we didn't miss it . . ." Just as it seems they will have to give up their search, Rupert suddenly remembers his Uncle Polar. "Of course!" he cries. "My uncle lives somewhere near here. Let's ask him to help us." The others agree and fly on until a solitary igloo comes into sight. "That's his house," calls Rupert. "Land outside and I'll introduce you both."

The plane taxis to a halt on the frozen snow and Rupert hurries towards the igloo. He rings the bell and waits for a reply. At first nothing happens, then a huge white bear peers out from the narrow doorway. "Uncle Polar!" cries Rupert. "Bless me!" laughs his uncle. "What a pleasant surprise! How nice to see you, Rupert, but what brings you to this part of the world? Come inside and tell me all about it. Bring your friends too," he adds. "There's plenty of room . . .'

RUPERT STAYS IN AN IGLOO

Although the igloo looks quite small,
Inside it isn't cramped at all . . .

"You'll have to stay this evening, so
I'll ring your folks and let them know."

Next morning the Assistant brings
His compass as they pack their things.

"No need!" smiles Polar. "For I know
Exactly where we've got to go!"

"Come and sit down," says Uncle Polar. "You must be tired after such a long journey!" He listens carefully as Rupert describes their search for the North Pole. "It's not always easy to find," he says. "Why don't you stay overnight and let me take you in the morning?" "I've got to get back to Santa," says the Cowboy. "You two stay and I'll come to fetch you tomorrow . . ." Rupert agrees and asks Uncle Polar to telephone Nutwood and let his parents know he is safe and sound.

The next day, Uncle Polar is up bright and early, making preparations for the expedition. "We've got a long walk ahead of us," he tells Rupert. "It's a good idea to take a picnic lunch." "I'll bring my compass too!" declares the Assistant. "Would you like to borrow my map?" "No need for that," smiles Uncle Polar. "I already know the way to the Pole . . ." When everyone is wrapped up well, he opens the door of the igloo and leads the way out across the snow . . .

RUPERT SEES THE POLE IS MISSING

Across the snow, he starts to stride
Due North, with Rupert at his side.

But as the trio march along
The Assistant's sure something's wrong . . .

"Good gracious!" Uncle Polar cries,
Unable to believe his eyes . . .

"The mound that we're all standing on
Is the right place – but the Pole's gone!"

As they leave the igloo behind them and march through the crisp, white snow, Rupert asks his uncle how he manages to find the way. "It's easy when you know what to look for," he laughs. "All you have to do is follow your nose!" "Pardon me for asking," says the Assistant, "but are you sure we're still going in the right direction? My compass is pointing more to the West . . ." "Nonsense!" growls Uncle Polar. "There must be something wrong with it! We're almost there . . ."

As the three companions continue on their way, it is Uncle Polar's turn to look puzzled. He stops, peers into the distance, walks a few paces forward, then comes to a complete halt. "It's gone!" he cries. "Sorry?" asks Rupert. "The North Pole!" gasps Uncle Polar. "It's been here since I was a cub. Now it's . . . disappeared!" Sure enough, when they reach the spot where the Pole should stand, there is nothing to be seen but a small hole in the ice!

RUPERT'S UNCLE HAS AN IDEA

"Look!" Rupert cries. "Someone's been here.
Their footprints still look very clear."

"Thieves!" Polar growls. "I'm sure that they
Removed the Pole and sailed away!"

"We'll find them!" the Assistant cries.
"My compass still shows where it lies . . ."

"Good!" Polar cries. "Now, follow me!
We'll chase their boat across the sea . . ."

What can have happened to the North Pole? As his uncle stares at the hole in the ice, Rupert spots a trail of footprints. "Look!" he cries. "Someone's been here before us!" "You don't think they took the Pole?" gasps the Assistant. "We'll soon find out!" growls Uncle Polar and starts to follow the tracks across the snow. To Rupert's surprise, they come to a sudden halt, where the ice meets the open sea. "Hrrumph!" cries Uncle Polar. "They must have left here in a boat!"

"If only *we* had a boat!" groans the Assistant. "Then we'd be able to follow them! My compass is still pointing towards the Pole, you see. All we have to do to find out where it's been taken is to keep going in the same direction . . ." "You're right!" cries Uncle Polar. "But there's no need for a boat, just follow me!" With that he leaps across to a large ice floe that's floating nearby. "Come on!" he calls to Rupert. "There's plenty of room here for us all!"

RUPERT SAILS ON AN ICE FLOE

*The pair jump on, but neither know
How Polar plans to use the floe . . .*

*Then, from his pocket, Polar brings
A little bell he kneels and rings . . .*

*Up pops a walrus, Wallace, who
Asks Polar what he wants to do.*

*He pushes them along as they
Use the compass to find the way.*

With the Assistant's compass to point the way, Uncle Polar seems sure that they will find the missing Pole. "Well done!" he cries as Rupert jumps across to join him. "This ice floe will make a splendid boat!" "Of course!" gasps the Assistant. "But how will you make it go in the right direction?" "Don't worry about that," laughs Polar and pulls a little silver bell from his pocket. "Quiet now," he whispers and starts to ring it, just above the water's surface.

For a long time nothing happens. Then there is a sudden splash and up pops a huge walrus! "This is an old friend of mine, called Wallace," explains Uncle Polar and tells the Walrus all about the missing Pole and how they hope to find it again. "Happy to help you!" cries Wallace and starts to push against the ice floe with all his might. Soon the friends are gliding through the water, with the Assistant giving directions while Rupert keeps watch for any strange ships.

RUPERT SPOTS A SHIP

Ahead of them they spot a boat
Above which snow clouds seem to float . . .

No wonder that the ship's so slow,
Its decks are thick with ice and snow!

As Uncle Polar climbs aboard
The crew run off. "A bear that roared!"

Then Rupert spots a look out, who
Has been forgotten by the crew . . .

Peering into the distance, Rupert spots some menacing dark clouds. The compass is pointing straight towards what looks like a giant snowstorm! "I can see a ship on the horizon!" he calls suddenly. "You're right!" gasps Uncle Polar. "Quick, Wallace! We mustn't lose sight of it!" As they draw nearer to the strange ship, Rupert can see that its decks are covered in a thick layer of snow. "How odd!" he murmurs. "It looks as if the blizzard has been following her for days . . ."

The ship is so heavily laden with snow that it can hardly move through the water. "Push us alongside, Wallace," calls Uncle Polar and gets ready to clamber aboard. As soon as they see him the sailors give a cry of alarm and run for their cabins as fast as they can. "Come back!" calls Uncle Polar, but by the time the Assistant and Rupert have joined him on deck there is no-one to be seen. No-one, that is, except a young look-out, who peers nervously down from the rigging.

RUPERT FINDS THE NORTH POLE

*"Don't be afraid!" says Rupert. "We
Must see your captain urgently . . ."*

*The Captain peers around the door
But dares not come out any more.*

*"I only want to let you know –
The North Pole's what attracts this snow!"*

*The Captain blinks. "I'd no idea!
In that case you can have it. Here!"*

"I don't know why everyone ran away!" shrugs Uncle Polar. "Never mind," says Rupert. "Let's talk to the look-out." Telling the boy not to be frightened, Rupert asks him how long the ship has been caught in the blizzard. "Ever since the captain came back from the North Pole," replies the boy. Rupert smiles and asks him to take them to the Captain's cabin. "Visitors, sir!" calls the boy. The door opens a crack and the Captain peers out anxiously . . .

"I hear you've been to the North Pole," says Uncle Polar, sternly. "Y . . yes," replies the Captain. "I'm an explorer." "And you've taken the Pole as a souvenir!" cries Rupert. "How did you know?" gasps the Captain. "Because it's a snow magnet," says Rupert. "That's why there's a blizzard following your ship . . ." The Captain blinks in astonishment. "I had no idea! In that case, you're welcome to it! The sooner it's back in it's rightful place, the better!"

RUPERT RETURNS THE POLE

"Goodbye!" the look out calls as he
Sees Rupert's ice floe put to sea.

The walrus pushes them once more
Across the water, to the shore.

"Thanks, Wallace!" Polar says, then he
Strides back to where the Pole should be.

He hands the Pole to Rupert when
It's time to put it back again . . .

"We're ready to go now, Wallace!" calls Uncle Polar. Holding the Pole carefully, he clambers back over the ship's rail and is soon helping Rupert and the Assistant back on to the ice floe. "Goodbye!" calls the look-out as they begin to glide away from the ship. "And thank you for saving us from the blizzard . . ." "We'll soon put things right now!" smiles Uncle Polar as the ice floe nears the shore. "Explorers indeed! Fancy trying to take the Pole home!"

As soon as the ice floe is near enough, Uncle Polar leaps off and helps the others to scramble ashore. "Well done, Wallace!" he tells his friend. "Without your help, we'd never have caught that ship!" Following the footprints back across the snow, he leads the way to the stone circle and hands the Pole to Rupert. "It's only right that you should put it back," he tells him. "If it hadn't been for you, no-one would have realised what was wrong." "Bravo!" cries the Assistant.

RUPERT FLIES BACK

*Then Polar telephones to tell
Santa that things have turned out well . . .*

*The Little Cowboy's plane appears.
"I hear you've found the Pole!" he cheers.*

*"Goodbye!" waves Rupert's uncle. Then
The little plane flies off again.*

*"That must be the explorer's ship.
Now they've escaped the snowstorm's grip . . ."*

As soon as the North Pole is safely back in place, Uncle Polar sets off across the snow towards his cosy igloo. While Rupert and the Assistant have a warm drink, he telephones Santa Claus to let him know that the mystery of the missing snow has been solved. "Splendid news!" says Santa. "I'll send the Little Cowboy to collect Rupert and his friend." Before long, Rupert hears the sound of a plane approaching and hurries out to see the Little Cowboy coming in to land.

"Goodbye, Rupert!" calls Uncle Polar as the plane takes off. "Glad I was able to help. Come and see me again soon!" Rupert promises that he will and waves to his uncle as the Little Cowboy flies off over the frozen snow and ice. "Look!" cries Rupert as they head out to sea. "There's the explorer's ship!" No longer icebound, the ship has at last escaped from the blizzard and is sailing steadily south. "I wonder if the look-out can see us?" thinks Rupert and waves at the ship.

RUPERT TRIES HIS NEW SLEDGE

*The Weather Clerk tells Rupert how
The snow's heading for Nutwood now.*

*The Cowboy cries, "Let's go and see!"
And off they fly immediately . . .*

*As Nutwood reappears below
The sky is full of falling snow!*

*The Cowboy stays behind and tries
Out Rupert's sledge. "Yippee!" he cries.*

Flying up above the clouds, the Little Cowboy carries on until he spots the distant towers of the Weather Station. The Clerk of the Weather is delighted to hear that the North Pole is back in place and tells Rupert that the clouds he sent should be well on their way to Nutwood. After saying goodbye to the Assistant, Rupert and the Cowboy climb into the plane and take off once more. "It won't be long before you're home!" calls the Cowboy as they start to gather speed.

"Look!" cries Rupert excitedly as Nutwood comes into view. "It's started snowing at last!" Down below he spots some of his pals, who are busy making a snowman. As soon as the plane lands he runs home to fetch his new sledge. "Come on!" he calls to the Little Cowboy. "Let's both go and try it out . . ." "Yippee!" cries the Cowboy as the pair whizz downhill. "If your Uncle Polar was here, I think he'd feel right at home!" The End.

Follow **Rupert** every day

in the **Daily Express**

ANSWERS TO PUZZLE:
Spot the Difference: (page 44) 1. Billy Goat's knapsack missing; 2. Cuff button missing from Billy Goat's jacket; 3. Middle button missing from Billy Goat's jacket; 4. Broken egg shell missing; 5. Handle missing from drawer; 6. Wrapper missing from butter; 7. Mrs. Bear's spoon missing; 8. Handle missing from cupboard; 9. Dates missing from calendar; 10. Door handle missing.

Three more pictures to colour . . .